Name _____

Chapter 1

Sections 3 & 4

Simplify.

D1716131

_____ 1. $4.2 + (-5.1) - (-2)$

_____ 2. $\frac{3}{10} - \frac{5}{12}$

_____ 3. $8 + |-8|$

_____ 4. Before adding or subtracting fractions, one must first get a common _____.

_____ 5. At the beginning of the month, a checkbook's balance was $345.23. A check was written on the tenth of the month for $127.54. Then a deposit was made on the fifteenth for $187.86. Checks for $125.26 and $87.01 were written on the eighteenth. Finally, $0.76 of interest was added at the end of the month. What was the ending balance of the checkbook?

_____ 6. Which of the following properties is illustrated by $(x + 3) + 0 = x + 3$?
   a. Associative Property of Addition
   b. Commutative Property of Addition
   c. Additive Identity Property
   d. Additive Inverse Property
   e. None of the above

Algebra 1

Chapter 1

Sections 5 & 6

Simplify.

_____ 1. -18×6

_____ 2. $-204 \div (-6)$

_____ 3. $73.5 \div 2.1$

_____ 4. Convert 8 in. to centimeters (remember 2.54 cm = 1 in.).

_____ 5. Which of the following are positive? List all correct answers.
    a. $-(-3)(2)(-4)$
    b. $(-3)(4)(-523)(0)$
    c. $\frac{3}{2} \times \frac{5}{-7}$
    d. $-34(-5)$

_____ 6. Which of the following is equivalent to $-24 \div 6$? List all correct answers.
    a. the ratio of -24 to 6
    b. the ratio of 6 to -24
    c. the quotient of -24 and 6
    d. -24 divided into 6
    e. -24 divided by 6

Sections 7 & 8

Simplify.

_____ 1. $(x^2)^3$

_____ 2. -2^{-4}

_____ 3. $8^2 + 4 \times 4$

_____ 4. Write your answer as a power of 3.
$(3^{-2})^4 \times 3^3 \div 3^{-3}$

_____ 5. If there are no grouping symbols, which operation is performed first?
   a. addition
   b. division
   c. exponentiation
   d. multiplication
   e. subtraction

_____ 6. When the following expression is simplified, which operation is performed first?
$9 + 3^2|2 + 7 \cdot 2(3 - 5)|$

Test Chapter 1

Simplify.

_____ 1. $-4(15)$ _____ 2. $-5 - (-2)$

_____ 3. $-6 - 2 + 5 - (-2)$ _____ 4. $(-2)(-8)(-4)$

_____ 5. $(-3)^2$ _____ 6. 8^0

_____ 7. $-90 \div (-6)$ _____ 8. $|12| - |-3|$

_____ 9. $-\frac{3}{8} + \frac{5}{12}$ _____ 10. $-\frac{10}{21}\left(-\frac{9}{25}\right)$

_____ 11. $\frac{12}{35} \div \left(-\frac{8}{25}\right)$ _____ 12. $3 + 2(4 - 6 \div 2 \times 3)$

_____ 13. $-3(4 + |3 - 2| + 2)$ _____ 14. $-|-|3||$

_____   15. Convert 26.2 mi to kilometers using 1 mi = 1.6 km.

_____   16. Translate the phrase to a numerical expression, then evaluate the
                           expression: the sum of the reciprocal of two and the opposite of three.

17. Graph each point on the number line.
    A: −6; B: 2.5; C: −$3\frac{1}{4}$; D: 7

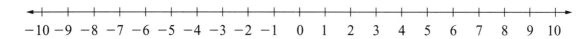

18. A segment has endpoints with coordinates −3 and 4.
_____   a. Find the length of the segment.

_____   b. Find the coordinate of the segment's midpoint.

19. Label the five subsets of the real numbers illustrated in the diagram below.

Real Numbers

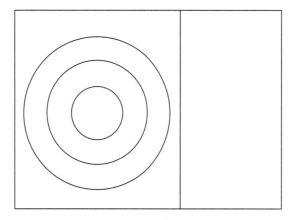

20. Place each of the following numbers in the appropriate area of the diagram above to illustrate the
    set(s) to which they belong: −2, 3, $\frac{1}{4}$, $\sqrt{5}$.

Using the following sets, list the result of each set operation and sketch a Venn diagram illustrating the operation. $A = \{1, 2, 3, 4, 5, 6\}$, $B = \{2, 4, 6, 8, 10, 12\}$, and $C = \{3, 6, 9, 12\}$

_____ 21. $A \cup C =$

_____ 22. $B \cap C =$

Name the property illustrated by each equation.

23. $-10 + 8 = 8 + (-10)$

24. $-8(-5 + 3) = -8(-5) + (-8)(3)$

25. What conclusion can you draw about a nonzero real number if its absolute value is equal to its opposite?

Chapter 2

Sections 1 & 2

Translate the following word phrases into algebraic expressions.

_____ 1. three less than twice a number

_____ 2. the amount a trucker earns in a week if he makes x deliveries at \$100 per delivery and driving y miles at \$0.25 per mile

_____ 3. List the variable(s) in the equation $C = 2\pi r$.

_____ 4. Which of the following does *not* indicate multiplication?
   a. product
   b. of
   c. times
   d. increased
   e. doubled

_____ 5. Evaluate the expression $(x + y)(x^2 + y^2)$ when $x = 3$ and $y = -4$.

_____ 6. Find the perimeter of a track with the following dimensions.

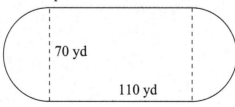

70 yd

110 yd

Chapter 2

Sections 3 & 4

_____ 1. Which of the following terms is like $3x^4$? List all correct answers.
   a. $3y^4$
   b. $3x^2$
   c. $12xy$
   d. $12x^4$
   e. $4x^3$

Simplify.

_____ 2. $26x^2 + 3y - 15x^2 - 8y$

_____ 3. $6(3x^2 - 5x + 1)$

Solve.

_____ 4. $x - 3.2 = 4.8$

_____ 5. $\frac{y}{3} = \frac{4}{9}$

6. Write a one-sentence summary of how to simplify algebraic expressions.

Algebra 1

Chapter 2

Sections 5 & 6

_____ 1. In which step of solving a word problem should the main unknown be identified?
   a. Read
   b. Plan
   c. Solve
   d. Check

Solve.

_____ 2. $3x + 17 = 38$ _____ 3. $3.2 + 2(y - 1.2) = 12.8$

_____ 4. $-\dfrac{y}{3} + 2 = 11$ _____ 5. Find the common fraction equivalent to $0.\overline{12}$.

_____ 6. Write and solve an equation to answer the following question. The Smith family rented a recreational vehicle for a seven-day vacation. The cost to rent the recreational vehicle was $80 per day plus $0.50 per mile. How many miles were driven if the total cost was $1350?

Chapter 2

Sections 7 & 8

Solve.

_____ 1. $5x + 10 = 2x - 5$

_____ 2. $10a + 2 - 5(a + 1) = 5a - 3$

_____ 3. Write an equivalent equation without fractions and then solve for the variable. $\frac{2x}{3} + \frac{1}{6} = \frac{1}{4}$

Write and solve an equation to answer the following questions.

_____ 4. Find three consecutive even integers such that five times the smallest is four times the largest.

_____ 5. A cashier always starts the day with $60 in pennies, nickels, dimes, and quarters. She begins with five times as many pennies as quarters, and the number of nickels and dimes are both twice the number of quarters. How many pennies does she start with?

6. State the property that justifies the illustrated step in solving the equation.

$3x + 4 - 2x + 5 = 6x + 2$

$3x - 2x + 4 + 5 = 6x + 2$

Chapter 2

Test

Use 2x − 10 + 5y to answer questions 1 and 2.

_____ 1. Name the constants.

_____ 2. Name the variables.

_____ 3. Which of the following terms are like $3x^2y$? List all correct responses.
   a. $3xy$
   b. $3x^2y^2$
   c. $-10x^2y$
   d. $12xy^2$
   e. $12x^2y$

_____ 4. When solving multi-step problems, which of the following is normally done first?
   a. Undo the addition or subtraction of the constant term.
   b. Undo the multiplication or division done to the variable.
   c. Move all variable terms to one side of the equation.
   d. Eliminate any parentheses or brackets from both sides.

5. Which property justifies the procedure used to eliminate fractions and decimals from equations?

6. Which property is used to remove parentheses in mathematical expressions and equations?

_____ 7. Evaluate $2x^2 + 3x - 10$ for the domain $\{-2, 3\}$.

_____ 8. Find the area, A, and perimeter, p, of a rectangle if the length is 12 cm and the width is 7 cm.

_____ 9. Find the volume, V, of a box with a height of 15 in. and a length and width of 12 in.

_____ 10. For the following question, use the equation $d = rt$, in which d is distance, r is rate, and t is time. How far is Grandmother's house if you must drive 4.5 hr through the woods at an average of 52 mi/hr to get there?

Simplify.

_____ 11. $3a - (a + 4)$

_____ 12. $3.5x(2x + 3) - 3x(x + 1.5)$

Solve.

_____ 13. $x + \frac{3}{4} = \frac{5}{8}$

_____ 14. $\frac{3x}{2} = -\frac{12}{7}$

_____ 15. $3b + 8 = 29$

_____ 16. $4(c + 5) - 2c = 14$

_____ 17. $12y + 3 = 7(y + 1) + 6$

_____ 18. $\frac{2x + 3}{4} + \frac{x - 1}{6} = \frac{x + 4}{3}$

Translate each of the following into an algebraic expression or equation.

_____ 19. seven more than four times a number

_____ 20. the square of the difference of two numbers

_____ 21. The absolute value of a number is the same as the product of five and the number.

Write and solve an equation to answer the following questions.

_____ 22. A tow truck charges a service fee of $50 and an additional fee of $1.75 per mile. What distance was Marcos's car towed if he received a bill for $71?

_____ 23. Find three consecutive integers such that the sum of the first and twice the second is equal to the third plus four.

_____ 24. Andre has $12.30 in pennies, nickels, dimes, and quarters. If he has the same number of each coin, how many of each does he have?

_____ 25. A pitcher needs more than one pitch to be effective. Dizzy uses his changeup only half as much as his fastball, and to save his arm, he throws a slider a third as much as his fastball. In a 110-pitch game, how many sliders would he throw?

Chapter 3

Sections 1 & 2

_____ 1. Which of the following is *not* a literal equation?
- a. $A = s^2$
- b. $C = 10\pi$
- c. $d = rt$
- d. $E = mc^2$
- e. $F = 9.8m$

_____ 2. Which is cheapest per ounce: a 2 L bottle (67.6 oz) of root beer at \$1.49, a six-pack of 20 oz bottles at \$2.49, or a twelve-pack of 12 oz cans at \$2.99?
- a. 2 L bottle
- b. six-pack
- c. twelve-pack

_____ 3. A recipe calls for 6 oz of chocolate to make 2 dozen cookies. How much chocolate is needed to make 100 cookies?

Solve.

_____ 4. $5(a - b) = 3(a + c)$ for a

_____ 5. $\dfrac{x - 2}{7} = \dfrac{x + 3}{12}$

_____ 6. $\dfrac{7x - 2}{3x + 4} = -\dfrac{5}{3}$

Chapter 3

Sections 3 & 4

For questions 1 and 2, use the fact that the two pentagons are similar.

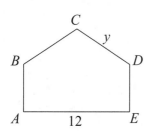 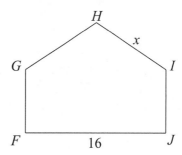

_____   1. If $x = 6$, find y.

_____   2. If the area of the smaller pentagon is 36, what is the area of the larger pentagon?

_____   3. The distance between Los Angeles and New York on a map is 19.5 in. Use the map's scale of 1 in. : 125 mi to determine the actual distance between New York and Los Angeles.

_____ 4. Find 72% of 340.

_____ 5. What percent of 1600 is 240?

_____ 6. It is estimated that the cost of room, board, and tuition is only about 80% of the total cost of attending college. If the cost of room, board, and tuition is $21,000 at a certain Christian college, what will be the estimated total cost of attending there?

Chapter 3
Sections 5 & 6

True or false.

_____ 1. A $10 increase for a $100 item is a larger percent change than a $10 increase for a $1000 item.

_____ 2. The retail price is the amount a merchant pays for the merchandise he sells.

Solve.

_____ 3. Find the percent change from 250 to 150.

_____ 4. Find both the experimental error and the percent error if the known value is 200 mL and the experimental value is 195 mL.

_____ 5. A bookstore is advertising 25% off all books today. What is the sale price of a book that has a retail price of $18?

_____ 6. A retiree has $200,000 to invest and needs to make $13,000 with her investments. If she can invest in government bonds at 6% or investment-grade bonds at 8%, how much should she invest in each?

Driving at 45 mi/hr, Angie leaves the town of Gunnison. Beth leaves one hour later driving the same route at 55 mi/hr. After some time passes, she catches up with Angie.

1. Using t to represent Beth's driving time, fill in the table describing the motion of each person.

	r	t	d
Angie			
Beth			

2. State an equation relating the distances traveled by each person.

3. How long does it take for Beth to catch up with Angie?

Ten gallons of a 25% salt solution are to be obtained by mixing a dilute 13% salt solution and a concentrated 33% salt solution.

4. Using x to represent the amount of dilute solution, fill in the table describing the solutions.

	Amount of Solution	%	Amount of Salt
Dilute			
Concentrate			
Mix			

5. State an equation relating the amount of salt in the solutions.

6. Solve the equation to find how many gallons of the dilute solution and how many gallons of the concentrated solution are needed.

Chapter 3

Test

_____ 1. What is the minimum number of variables a literal equation must have?

_____ 2. Because they have different expressions representing the same quantity in the numerator and denominator, _____ are used to convert rates to equivalent rates that have different units.

_____ 3. A statement of equality between two ratios is called a _____.
   a. percentage
   b. product
   c. property
   d. proportion
   e. relation

_____ 4. All _____ are similar.
   a. triangles
   b. squares
   c. right triangles
   d. rectangles
   e. polygons

_____ 5. Convert 66 ft/sec to miles per hour.

_____ 6. State the unit rate if a car burns 150 gal on a 3000 mi trip.

_____ 7. Solve $\dfrac{2d + 3}{5} = \dfrac{3d - 6}{8}$.

_____ 8. Solve $5 = \dfrac{2m - b}{m + b}$ for m.

_____ 9. What percent of 65 is 52?

_____ 10. 45% of what number is 225?

Use the similar figures below to answer questions 11–13.

_____ 11. Find w.

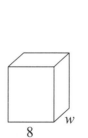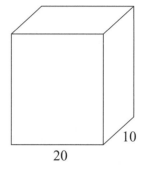

8   20   10

_____ 12. If the front face of the smaller figure has an area of 80, what is the area of the corresponding face of the larger figure?

_____ 13. If the volume of the larger figure is 3000, what is the volume of the smaller figure?

Name _____

_____ 14. If the distance between Green Bay, Wisconsin, and Spokane, Washington, is 1650 mi, and on a map the distance is 25 in., determine the scale of the map.

_____ 15. Gabriela was given a 15% increase in wages. If she earned $36,000 last year, what can she expect to earn this year?

_____ 16. The density of a particular brand of corn syrup is known to be 1360 g/L. If Ai-Lin determined the density to be 1372 g/L, then what is the percent error of Ai-Lin's experiment?

_____ 17. What are the markup and the retail price of a suit that costs a retailer $182 if he uses a standard markup rate of 30%?

_____ 18. A retailer marks up all merchandise 50%. If a pair of basketball shoes costs the retailer $100, how much will they cost a shopper if he finds the shoes on a discount rack that advertises all shoes on the rack to be 50% off retail price?

_____ 19. A local steakhouse advertises a dinner special for $10. What will the total price of the special be after paying 12% sales tax and tipping 15% on the total bill?

_____ 20. A car salesman earns $500 per week plus 1.5% commission on his sales. If he sold two cars for a total of $55,000 last week, how much did he make?

21. Grandma has $250,000 to invest. She divides her money into two accounts. One account is in ultra-safe treasury bills paying 4% interest, and the other is in riskier corporate bonds paying 6%. If she needs $12,000 per year in income from her investments, how much should she invest in each account?

_____

22. Steve bicycles 3 mi to school every day at 15 mi/hr. If school starts at 8:30 AM and he needs 15 min to lock his bike and get to his desk, then what time should he leave his house?

_____

23. The distance from Cleveland to Chicago is 345 mi. A train, traveling 45 mi/hr, leaves Chicago heading to Cleveland at the same time that another train, traveling 30 mi/hr, leaves Cleveland heading to Chicago. How far from Chicago will the two trains meet?

_____

24. How many gallons of ethanol are in a 100 gal mixture that is 10% ethanol?

_____

25. If Holstein cows produce milk that is on average 3.66% butterfat and Jersey cows produce milk that is on average 4.5% butterfat, how many gallons of Jersey milk should be added to every 100 gal of Holstein milk to have milk that is 4% butterfat?

© 2012 BJU Press. Reproduction prohibited.

CHAPTER 3 | TEST

Algebra 1   PAGE 4

Chapters 1-3

First Quarter Exam

Simplify.

_____ 1. $|-3|$

_____ 2. $5.3 - 2(4.1 - 1.6)$

_____ 3. $\frac{5}{6} - \frac{3}{10}$

_____ 4. $7 - |-7|$

_____ 5. $\frac{5}{12} \div \frac{10}{21}$

_____ 6. $-4^2 + (2 - 24 \div 4 \times 3)$

_____ 7. $6(x - y) + 5(x + y)$

Solve.

_____ 8. $x - 13 = 27$

_____ 9. $5x - 4.7 = 20.3$

_____ 10. $\frac{2y + 1}{6} = \frac{3y - 4}{10}$

_____ 11. $a(x + b) = c(x + d)$ for x

_____ 12. $3(x + 4) - 5(x - 4) = 2x + 4(x - 6)$

In questions 13 and 14, translate into an algebraic expression or equation.

_____ 13. The sum of x and y is five more than the difference between y and twice x.

_____ 14. The absolute value of the sum of a number and six.

_____ 15. Which of the following properties is illustrated by $(2x)x = 2(xx) = 2x^2$?
  a. Associative Property of Addition
  b. Associative Property of Multiplication
  c. Commutative Property of Addition
  d. Commutative Property of Multiplication
  e. Distributive Property

_____ 16. Let $A = \{1, 2, 3, 4, 5\}$ and $B = \{3, 4, 5\}$. Find $A \cap B$.
  a. $\varnothing$
  b. $\{1, 2\}$
  c. $\{3, 4, 5\}$
  d. $\{1, 2, 3, 4, 5\}$
  e. none of the above

_____ 17. Which is the best buy?
  a. a three-roll package of paper towels at $1.59 per package
  b. a twelve-roll package of paper towels at $4.99 per package
  c. a package of six double rolls at $4.59 per package
  d. a package of eight double rolls at $5.59 per package

_____ 18. Evaluate $x + y^2 \div 6 \div 2$ when $x = 7$ and $y = 12$.

_____ 19. Convert 40 km to miles using 1 mi $= 1.6$ km.

_____ 20. 280 is 14% of what number?

_____ 21. Convert 45 mi/hr to yards per second.

_____ 22. Convert $0.\overline{7}$ to fractional form.

23. Label the five subsets of the real numbers illustrated in the diagram below, and place each of the following numbers in the appropriate area of the diagram to illustrate the set(s) to which they belong: $-3, 0, 3, 3.03003003\ldots, 3.\overline{3}$.

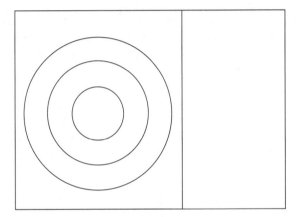

_____ 24. If the two triangles are similar and the area of the larger triangle is 36, find DF and the area of the smaller triangle.

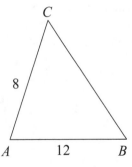

25. Write the formulas for the perimeter and the area of a square with the side, *s*, and a perimeter of 20 cm. Then find the area.

_____ a. the formulas

_____ b. the area

_____ 26. In an experiment to find the melting point of fudge, Stan measured the melting point at 237°F and Stacy measured it at 242°F. Find the percent difference between the two experimental values to two decimal places.

_____ 27. It was known that the actual length of the beam was 6.3 in. The class was asked to measure the beam using different types of measuring tapes. Demetrius's tape was accurate to one-eighth of an inch, so he measured the board to be 6.25 in. What was the percent error of his experiment to the nearest tenth of a percent?

_____ 28. A store owner marks up jeans 200%. If she sells a pair of designer jeans for $36, what did she pay for them?

_____ 29. Rick set out on his bike for a cookout at church, traveling at 10 mi/hr. Fifteen minutes later his mother, realizing that he had forgotten the hot dogs he signed up to bring, set out to catch him in the car. If she drove 40 mi/hr, how long did it take her to catch up with him?

_____ 30. One pound of deluxe mixed nuts containing 20% peanuts is mixed with two pounds of regular mixed nuts that are 50% peanuts. What percent of the mixture is peanuts?

Chapter 4

Sections 1 & 2

Multiple Choice. List all correct answers.

_____ 1. Which of the following is a solution to $z^2 + 2 < 6$?
   a. -4
   b. -2
   c. 0
   d. 2
   e. 4

_____ 2. Which of the following phrases means "is not greater than or equal to"?
   a. is at most
   b. is at least
   c. is more than
   d. is less than
   e. does not exceed

Solve and graph.

_____ 3. $x + 6 \geq 2$
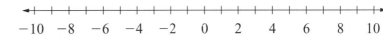

_____ 4. $-2x > -4$

Write an inequality and solve.

_____ 5. Find all the numbers such that the difference between the number and its opposite is at most 6.

_____ 6. A single trip on a toll road costs $1.20. Frequent users can get a monthly pass that costs $25. How many times a month must a person use the toll road before the monthly pass becomes a better deal?

Chapter 4

Section 3

Solve and graph.

_____ 1. $4 - 7x \le 18$

_____ 2. $20 + 6z > 12z - 13$

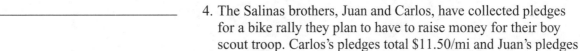

Write an inequality, but do not solve.

_____ 3. The high temperature for the day is predicted to be 86°F. Use the formula $F = \frac{9}{5}C + 32$ to write an inequality in degrees Celsius for the range of temperatures predicted.

_____ 4. The Salinas brothers, Juan and Carlos, have collected pledges for a bike rally they plan to have to raise money for their boy scout troop. Carlos's pledges total $11.50/mi and Juan's pledges total $9.75/mi. Carlos can peddle 10 mi/hr and Juan can peddle 12 mi/hr. If they plan to start and stop at the same time, how many hours will they have to bike if they want to raise at least $1000 together?

Algebra 1

Write an inequality and solve.

_____ 5. Find all numbers such that the number added to itself is less than that number subtracted from 6.

_____ 6. Asha feels she needs $45,000 per year in retirement. If she receives $2,500 a month from Social Security, at what interest rate must Asha invest her $250,000 of savings for her income to be at least $45,000 per year?

Sections 4 & 5

Graph.

1. $x \geq -1$ and $x < 2$

$\begin{array}{cccccccccccccc} \text{-6} & \text{-5} & \text{-4} & \text{-3} & \text{-2} & \text{-1} & 0 & 1 & 2 & 3 & 4 & 5 & 6 \end{array}$

2. $x > -5$ or $x > -2$

$\begin{array}{cccccccccccccc} \text{-6} & \text{-5} & \text{-4} & \text{-3} & \text{-2} & \text{-1} & 0 & 1 & 2 & 3 & 4 & 5 & 6 \end{array}$

Solve.

_____ 3. $x + 5 \geq 2$ and $-3x + 7 > 1$

_____ 4. $2x - 5 < 1$ or $-4x + 5 > 9$

_____ 5. Which compound inequality has the set of real numbers as the solution?
   a. $x < 5$ and $x \geq 5$
   b. $x < 5$ or $x > 10$
   c. $x < 3$ and $x > -2$
   d. $x \geq -3$ or $x < 7$
   e. $x < 3$ or $x < -2$

_____ 6. Which compound inequality has the empty set as the solution?
   a. $x < 5$ and $x \geq 5$
   b. $x < 5$ or $x > 10$
   c. $x < 3$ and $x > -2$
   d. $x \geq -3$ or $x < 7$
   e. $x < 3$ or $x < -2$

Chapter 4

Sections 6 & 7

Solve.

_____ 1. $|x + 5| = 6$

_____ 2. $|x - 7| < 3$

_____ 3. $|2x + 5| > 9$

_____ 4. $|-3x + 4| = -3$

_____ 5. Write an equation representing all numbers that are 3 units from 7.

_____ 6. Write an inequality representing all numbers that are at most 6 units from -2.

Chapter 4

Test

Graph.

1. $x < 5$

```
-6 -5 -4 -3 -2 -1  0  1  2  3  4  5  6
```

2. $x \geq -25$

```
-30    -20    -10     0    10    20    30
```

3. $|x| > 3$

```
-6 -5 -4 -3 -2 -1  0  1  2  3  4  5  6
```

4. $|x| \leq 5$

```
-6 -5 -4 -3 -2 -1  0  1  2  3  4  5  6
```

Solve.

_____ 5. $x - 15 \leq 8$ _____ 6. $-4x < 36$

_____ 7. $3x - 5 \leq x + 11$ _____ 8. $x + 4(x - 1) < 7 - 2x + 3$

Solve and graph.

_____ 9. $2 - x \leq 5$ and $2x + 1 \geq -8$

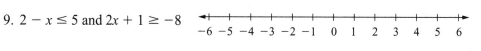

_____ 10. $4x \leq x$ or $3x < 6$

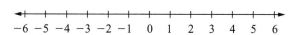

Match each inequality to its solution set.

_____ 11. $x \geq 2$ and $x < 2$ a. $\varnothing$

_____ 12. $x \geq 2$ or $x < 2$ b. $\{2\}$

_____ 13. $x \leq 2$ and $x \geq 2$ c. $x \neq 2$

_____ 14. $x > 2$ or $x < 2$ d. all real numbers

Match each phrase to the correct mathematical translation.

_____ 15. all numbers that are at most 5   a. $x > 5$

_____ 16. all numbers that exceed 5   b. $x < 5$

_____ 17. all numbers that are at least 5   c. $x \geq 5$

_____ 18. all numbers that are not greater than or equal to 5   d. $x \leq 5$

Solve.

_____ 19. $|4x - 10| = 22$

_____ 20. $|2x - 7| < 3$

_____ 21. $|3x + 2| \geq 0$

Write an equation and solve.

_____ 22. Ten less a number is at most six. Find the number.

_____ 23. Penny earned a 74% on her first test. If each test has 100 points, what must she earn on her next test to achieve an average of at least 80%?

_____ 24. Find all numbers such that twice the number is 7 units from 11.

25. Machine parts are manufactured with a given *tolerance*, the permissible limit of variation.

_____ a. Write an absolute value inequality representing the diameter of an engine cylinder that is to be 5 cm wide with a tolerance of ±0.005 cm.

_____ b. Then solve the inequality to state the range of acceptable diameters.

Chapter 5

Sections 1 & 2

Multiple Choice.

_____ 1. The first coordinate of the point $(-3, 2)$ indicates the point is located
_____.

 a. 3 units to the left of the y-axis
 b. 3 units to the right of the y-axis
 c. 3 units above the x-axis
 d. 3 units below the x-axis
 e. cannot be determined

_____ 2. In which quadrants are the first coordinates of all the points negative?
 a. I and II
 b. I and III
 c. I and IV
 d. II and III
 e. III and IV

_____ 3. State the coordinates of the point that is 5 units to the left and 6 units above the
point $(2, -3)$.

Use the relation $R = \{(2, 3), (1, 3), (-2, 1), (1, 1)\}$ for questions 4 and 5.

4. State the domain and the range.

5. Determine whether the relation is or is not a function and explain why.

_____ 6. If the function $f = \{(0, 3), (1, 7), (2, -3), (3, 1), (4, 5), (5, -2)\}$,
then $f(3) =$ ___.

Chapter 5

Sections 3 & 4

_____ 1. Which of the following graphs represent(s) a function? List all that apply.

a.    b.   c.   d.

Use the function $f = \{(x, y) \mid y = x^2 + 1\}$ for questions 2 and 3.

2. Complete the table of five ordered pairs and graph the function.

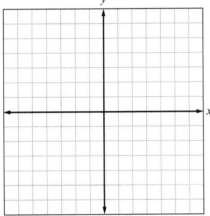

x	-2	-1	0	1	2
y					

3. State the domain and range of the function.

**David's Distance from Home
when Commuting from Work**

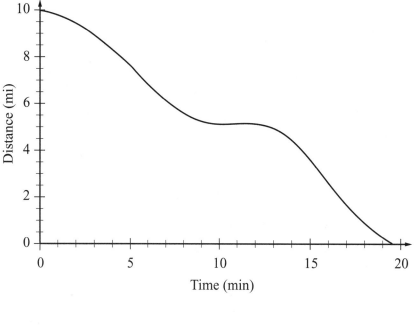

_____ 4. How far does David live from work?

_____ 5. When was David stopped at a light?
  a. at 1 min   b. at 5 min   c. at 8 min
  d. at 11 min   e. at 15 min   f. at 20 min

_____ 6. When was David driving the fastest?
  a. at 1 min   b. at 5 min   c. at 8 min
  d. at 11 min   e. at 15 min   f. at 20 min

Chapter 5

Section 5

Consider the following function, f, from the table for questions 1–3.

x	-2	-1	0	1	2
y	4	2	0	c	-4

_____ 1. Find c.

_____ 2. State the function rule.

_____ 3. What is $f(2.5)$?

For questions 4–6, consider the following situation: Ink cartridges for your printer can be purchased either online or at a local office supply store. The online company charges $4 per cartridge plus $20 shipping and handling. The local office supply store charges $5.50 per cartridge.

_____ 4. Write a function rule for the cost to buy x cartridges online.

_____ 5. Write a function rule for the cost to buy x cartridges at your local office supply store.

_____ 6. How many cartridges would you have to order before it costs less to buy them online than at the store?

Name _____

Chapter 5

Sections 6 & 7

_____ 1. If y varies directly with x and y doubles, then x _____.

x	y
0	0
1	10
2	5
5	2

_____ 2. State whether the table represents a direct variation, an indirect variation, or neither.

_____ 3. If s varies inversely with t and $s = 12$ when $t = 8$, write the function rule. Then find s when $t = 3$.

_____ 4. State the vertex of $f(x) = |x - 3| + 2$.

5. Describe the translation of the graph of $f(x) = |x|$ that produces the graph of $f(x) = |x - 3| + 2$.

6. Plot at least 3 points of $f(x) = |x - 3| + 2$, including the vertex and at least one point on each side of the vertex. Then graph the function.

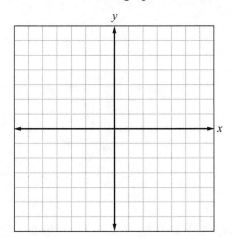

Chapter 5

Test

True or false.

_____ 1. Every relation is a function.

_____ 2. If every vertical line intersects the graph of a relation in one point or not at all, then the relation is a function.

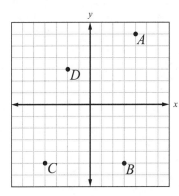

Use the graph to the right to answer questions 3 and 4.

_____ 3. State the coordinates of point *A*.

_____ 4. Which point is in quadrant II?

Use the graphs of the two relations below to answer questions 5–7.

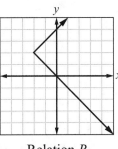

Relation *R*

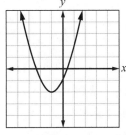

Relation *S*

_____ 5. Which of the above relation(s) is a function?

_____ 6. What is the domain of *R*?

_____ 7. What is the range of *S*?

Johnny throws a ball from the top edge of a canyon and then watches it fall until it hits the canyon floor. The graph of the height, in feet, of the ball above the canyon at time *t* is given on the right. Use the graph to answer the following questions.

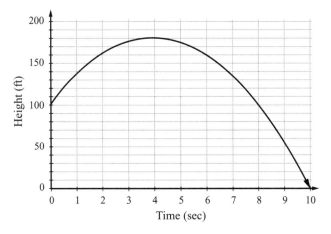

_____ 8. How high is the top edge of the canyon above the canyon floor?

_____ 9. What was the maximum height of the ball above the canyon floor?

_____ 10. At what time did the ball reach its maximum height?

_____ 11. When did the ball hit the canyon floor?

Use the function rule *f*(*x*) = −*x* + 2 for questions 12 and 13.

_____ 12. List the ordered pairs for the domain {−1, 0, 2}.

13. Graph the function *f*(*x*), assuming the domain is all real numbers.

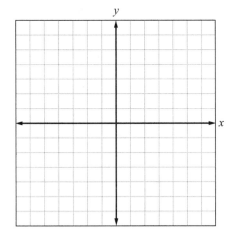

_____ 14. Which of the following graphs represents a direct variation?

a. 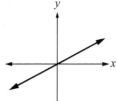   b. 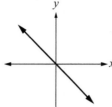   c.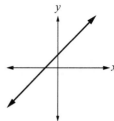

d. 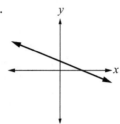   e.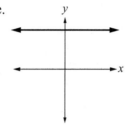

15. If y varies inversely with x and y triples, then what happens to x?

16. If y is directly proportional to x and y is 12 when $x = 10$, …

_____ a. state the constant of variation.

_____ b. write the function rule describing the variation.

_____ c. find y when x is 25.

17. If y varies inversely with x and $y = 14$ when $x = 3$, …

_____ a. state the constant of variation.

_____ b. write the function rule describing the variation.

_____ c. find y when x is 7.

18. Describe the translation of the graph of $y = |x|$ that produces the graph of $f(x) = |x + 3|$.

19. Describe the translation of the graph of $y = |x|$ that produces the graph of $f(x) = |x| + 3$.

_____ 20. What is the vertex of the graph of $f(x) = |x + 7| - 4$?

Name _____

Chapter 6

1. Using convenient values for x in the equation $y = 2x - 3$, make a table of at least three ordered pairs and graph the equation.

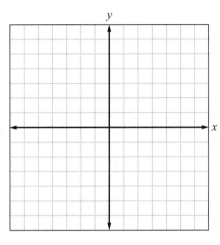

_____   2. Find the x- and y- intercepts of the linear equation $4x + 2y = 6$.

　　　　　　　　　　　a. x-intercept

_____   b. y-intercept

_____   3. What is the slope of the line in the graph below?

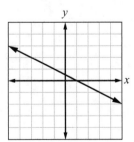

_____   4. Find the slope of the line passing through (5, 7) and (3, 11).

Department Store Sales

_____ 5. What was the yearly rate of increase in sales from the second year until the fifth year?

_____ 6. If the store had not suspended its sales campaign in its fifth year, and if sales continue to increase at the same rate they increased for the previous three years, predict the store's sales revenue in its fifteenth year of operation.

Chapter 6

Sections 3 & 4

_____ 1. Which equation could be the equation of the line?

   a. $y = 3x - 2$
   b. $y = 3x + 2$
   c $y = -3x - 2$
   d. $y = -3x + 2$
   e. none of the above

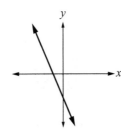

_____ 2. Write the slope-intercept form of the equation of the line passing through $(0, 3)$ with a slope of -2.

_____ 3. Write the slope-intercept form of the equation of the line passing through $(3, 2)$ with a slope of 4.

_____ 4. Write the slope-intercept form of the equation of the line passing through $(4, -1)$ and $(6, -7)$.

Hooke's law states that the length that a spring is stretched is proportional to the applied force. A pan hangs from a 50 cm spring. When a 10 kg mass is placed in the pan, it stretches the spring 6 cm.

_____ 5. Write a function rule $l(w)$ that models the length of the spring based on the mass of the object in the pan.

_____ 6. What is the mass of an object in the pan if the spring is stretched to a length of 65 cm?

Chapter 6

Section 5

_____ 1. The equation of line l is $y = 3x + 2$.
a. What is the slope of a line parallel to l?

_____ b. What is the slope of a line perpendicular to l?

_____ 2. Write the slope-intercept form of the equation of the line passing through $(3, 2)$ and parallel to $2x - y = 5$.

_____ 3. Write the slope-intercept form of the equation of the line passing through $(4, -1)$ and perpendicular to $3x + 12y = 5$.

_____ 4. Which of the following could be a pair of equations for the two perpendicular lines shown in the graph?

    a. $y = x + 3$ and $y = -x + 3$

    b. $y = 2x$ and $y = -2x + 3$

    c. $y = -2x$ and $y = \frac{1}{2}x + 3$

    d. $y = 2x$ and $y = -\frac{1}{2}x + 3$

    e. $y = x$ and $y = -x - 3$

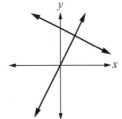

A (3, 5), B (−2, 6), and C (0, 16) are the vertices of a triangle.

5. Find the slope of each segment.

_____   a. $m_{\overline{AB}}$

_____   b. $m_{\overline{BC}}$

_____   c. $m_{\overline{AC}}$

6. Is the triangle a right triangle? Explain your reasoning.

Chapter 6

Sections 6 & 7

Use the scatterplots below to answer questions 1 and 2.

a.
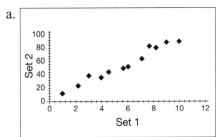

b.
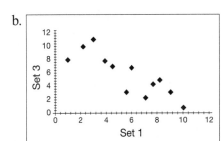

c.
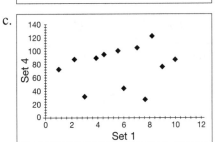

d.
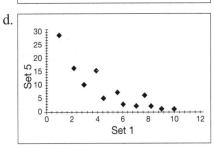

_____ 1. Which scatterplot above indicates a strong positive linear correlation? List all correct answers.

_____ 2. Which data set is least correlated with Set 1?

_____ 3. Is the point $(0, 5)$ a solution to $y < -3x + 7$?

4. Graph the inequality $x - 3y \geq 6$.

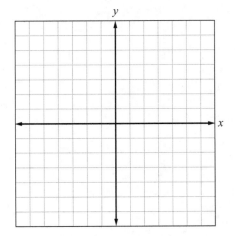

A teacher gives 5 points for correctly completing an "easy" homework question and 10 points for correctly completing a "challenge" question. To get an A on a homework assignment, the student must get at least 100 points.

_____ 5. Using x to represent the number of easy questions and y the number of challenge questions, write an inequality that models the number of questions a student needs to complete correctly in order to earn an A on an assignment.

_____ 6. If there are fifteen easy questions in a homework set, what is the minimum number of challenge questions a student must correctly complete in order to earn an A on the homework assignment?

Chapter 6

Test

Multiple Choice. List all correct answers.

_____ 1. Which of the following is a linear equation?
  a. $3x - 4y = 3$
  b. $2x^2 - 3y^2 = 5$
  c. $y = 2x - 5$
  d. $x = 5y + 21$
  e. $\frac{3}{x} + \frac{4}{y} = 2$

_____ 2. If $A(x_1, y_1)$ and $B(x_2, y_2)$ are two points on a line, which of the following formulas represents the slope of the line?
  a. $m = \dfrac{y_2 - y_1}{x_2 - x_1}$

  b. $m = \dfrac{x_2 - x_1}{y_2 - y_1}$

  c. $m = \dfrac{y_1 - y_2}{x_2 - x_1}$

  d. $m = \dfrac{y_2 - y_1}{x_1 - x_2}$

  e. $m = \dfrac{y_1 - y_2}{x_1 - x_2}$

_____ 3. What is the slope of the graphed line?
  a. $\frac{5}{2}$ b. $-\frac{5}{2}$

  c. $\frac{2}{5}$ d. $-\frac{2}{5}$
  e. none of the above

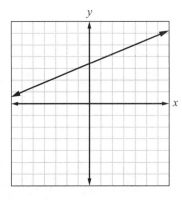

_____ 4. Which of the following quantities could be represented by the slope of a line?
  a. fixed costs of a business
  b. production cost per hour
  c. the speed of an object
  d. the final cost of a product
  e. the height of an object

_____ 5. Match the graphed line to its equation.
  a. $3x + 2y = 5$
  b. $3x - 2y = 5$
  c. $-3x + 2y = -5$
  d. $-3x - 2y = 5$
  e. $3x + 2y = -5$

6. Which of the following inequalities is represented by the graph?

a. $y < 3x + 3$
b. $y \leq 3x + 3$
c. $y > 3x + 3$
d. $y \geq 3x + 3$

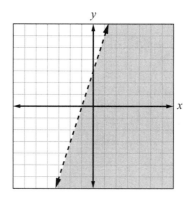

7. A company surveyed its workers to identify the most important factor in determining worker productivity. Which scatterplot exhibits the strongest linear correlation?

a.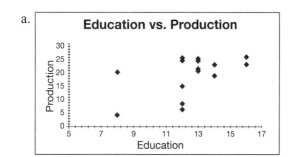

b.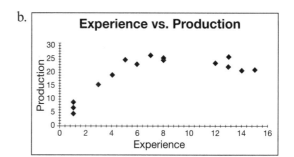

c.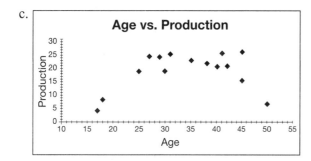

8. If $3x + 4y = 7$ is perpendicular to $8x + By = 2$, then what is B?

a. 8
b. −8
c. 6
d. −6
e. none of the above

9. Find the *x*- and *y*-intercepts of $4x - 3y = 24$.

_____   a. *x*-intercept

_____   b. *y*-intercept

10. Graph $y = 4x - 2$.

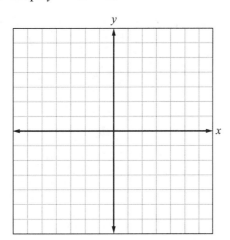

_____ 11. Find the slope of the line passing through $(3, 7)$ and $(14, -15)$.

12. State the slope and *y*-intercept of $3x + 2y = 8$.

_____   a. slope

_____   b. *y*-intercept

13. The equation of line *l* is $y = -2x + 3$.

_____   a. What is the slope of a line parallel to *l*?

_____   b. What is the slope of a line perpendicular to *l*?

Distance vs. Time

14. Steve leaves for work in his car and ten minutes later enters the freeway. Upon exiting the freeway he stops at a light and then proceeds to work. The graph above models his commute.

_____ a. What was his speed (in mi/hr) while traveling on the freeway?

_____ b. What was his average speed (in mi/hr) for the entire trip to work?

_____ 15. Write the equation of the line with a slope of -7 and a y-intercept of $(0, 2)$.

_____ 16. Write the equation of the line passing through $(3, 4)$ and $(3, -2)$.

_____ 17. Write the slope-intercept form of the equation of the line passing through $(2, 1)$ with a slope of -3.

_____ 18. Write the slope-intercept form of the equation of the line parallel to $2x + 4y = 8$ and passing through $(1, 2)$.

_____ 19. Write the equation of the line passing through $(3, 5)$ and perpendicular to $x = 3$.

20. A state's population is currently 5,000,000 and it is losing 125,000 residents each year.

_____   a. Write a linear function that represents the population of the state.

_____   b. How many years will it take the population to decline to 4,000,000?

_____ 21. A human's maximum heart rate is defined to be roughly 220 minus the person's age. Write an inequality to show the maximum heart rate, r, for a person of age a.

_____ 22. Determine which of the following ordered pairs are solutions to the inequality $y < 4x + 1$: $(0, 0)$, $(1, 5)$, $(-1, 6)$, $(2, 2)$.

The average life expectancy of someone living in the United States in 1970 was 71 yr. In 2000 the life expectancy had increased to 77 yr of age.

_____ 23. Write the equation of a line modeling this relationship.

_____ 24. Use the equation from the previous question to predict the year when life expectancy will reach 100 yr.

25. The scatterplot below illustrates the relationship between the ACT score and the grade point average (GPA) of college students participating in a study.

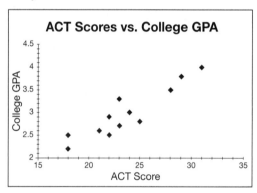

_____ a. Draw and write the equation of a trend line that models this relationship.

_____ b. Use your equation of the trend line to predict the GPA of someone with an ACT score of 25.

Name _____

Sections 1 & 2

_____ 1. Determine whether $(-3, 4)$ is a solution to the system.
$$2x - y = -10$$
$$3x + 4y = 1$$

_____ 2. Identify the solution to the system from its graph.

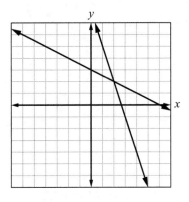

_____ 3. Solve by graphing.
$$2x + y = 4$$
$$x + 2y = -1$$

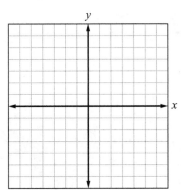

Algebra 1

Solve each system by substitution.

_____ 4. $y = x + 4$
$y = -2x + 1$

_____ 5. $5x + 2y = 1$
$x - 2y = 5$

_____ 6. Write a system of equations and solve the system by substitution. The sum of two numbers is 26, and the difference between three times the larger and twice the smaller is 18.

Chapter 7

Sections 3 & 4

Multiple Choice.

 1. Choose the best initial step in solving the following system by substitution.

$3x + 6y = 7$
$2x + 8y = 14$

a. Solve the first equation for x.
b. Solve the first equation for y.
c. Solve the second equation for x.
d. Solve the second equation for y.

 2. Determine the multipliers needed to eliminate the **y terms** in the system.

$4x + 9y = 7$
$3x - 12y = 11$

a. Multiply the first equation by 3 and the second by 4.
b. Multiply the first equation by -3 and the second by 4.
c. Multiply the first equation by 4 and the second by 3.
d. Multiply the first equation by 4 and the second by -3.

Solve.

_____ 3. Solve the system by substitution.

$3x - 6y = 15$
$2x + 8y = -2$

 4. Solve the system by elimination.

$5x - 2y = 3$
$2x + 3y = 24$

_____

5. Quick Cleaners offers the following specials: five shirts and two pairs of pants for $12.50 or ten shirts and three pairs of pants for $22.00. Write and solve a system of equations to find the charge for each shirt and pair of pants.

_____

6. Solve the system.

$$\frac{1}{3}x + \frac{1}{2}y = \frac{1}{12}$$

$$\frac{2}{5}x - \frac{3}{5}y = \frac{3}{10}$$

Chapter 7

Sections 5 & 6

Multiple Choice.

_____ 1. When graphed, an inconsistent system of two linear equations consists of
_____.
  a. coinciding lines
  b. intersecting lines
  c. parallel lines

Solve each system. Then classify it as consistent independent, consistent dependent, or inconsistent. If the solution is an entire line, state its equation in slope-intercept form.

2. $x - 2y = 6$
   $2x + 5y = 3$
_____ a. Solution

_____ b. Type

3. $8x + 5y = 10$
   $10y = -16x + 20$
_____ a. Solution

_____ b. Type

Andy canoed downriver for two hours and returned in three hours. Andy's speed in still water is 2 mi/hr faster than the speed of the current. What is Andy's still-water paddling speed and the speed of the current?

4. Complete the table describing the problem. Let w represent speed in still water and c represent speed of the current.

	r	t	d
Downstream			
Upstream			

5. Write a system of equations for the question.

6. Solve the system to answer the question.

"Peanuts Plus" contains 50% peanuts, whereas "Deluxe Nuts" contains only 25% peanuts. A vendor combines the two brands to produce 100 lb of mixed nuts containing 35% peanuts. How many pounds of each should be used?

1. Complete the table describing the problem. Let *x* represent pounds of "Peanuts Plus" and *y* represent pounds of "Deluxe Nuts."

	Quantity	% Peanuts	Total Amount of Peanuts
Plus			
Deluxe			
New Mix			

2. Write a system of equations for the problem.

3. Solve the system to answer the question.

_____ 4. Which region of the graph represents the solution to the system of inequalities?

$$y < -x + 2$$
$$y > 2x - 4$$

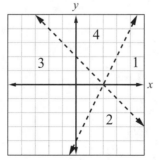

5. Graph the system of inequalities.

$y > 4x + 3$
$y \leq -x + 5$

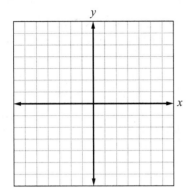

6. Tom is building a set of kennels as shown below. The width, w, must be at least 6 ft, and the length, l, must be at least 6 ft. Tom has 150 ft of fencing that he can use to build the kennels. Write a system of inequalities that models these constraints.

Chapter 7

Test

Determine whether the given point is a solution to each system.

_____ 1. $(1, -1)$
$$3x - 2y = 5$$
$$2x + 5y = -3$$

_____ 2. $(-2, -3)$
$$4x - 3y > 1$$
$$5x + 3y \leq -1$$

Multiple Choice.

_____ 3. Which system is easiest to solve by substitution?

    a. $3x + 3y = 5$
       $2x - 4y = 5$

    b. $2x - y = 4$
       $4x + 2y = 7$

    c. $5x + 3y = 9$
       $2x - 7y = 13$

    d. $2x + 3y = 6$
       $3y - 2x = 7$

_____ 4. Choose the best initial step in solving the system by substitution.

$$3x + y = 4$$
$$2x - 3y = 7$$

    a. Solve the first equation for x.

    b. Solve the first equation for y.

    c. Solve the second equation for x.

    d. Solve the second equation for y.

_____ 5. When the linear equations in a system of equations have different slopes and the same y-intercepts, the system is said to be _____.

    a. consistent independent

    b. consistent dependent

    c. inconsistent

_____ 6. When solving a system of linear equations produces a false statement such as $1 = 2$, the system is said to be _____.

    a. consistent independent

    b. consistent dependent

    c. inconsistent

7. Determine the multipliers needed to eliminate the **x terms** in the following system. Do not solve.

$$3x + 4y = 3$$
$$-5x + 2y = 6$$

Solve each system by graphing.

_____ 8. $y = 2x - 6$
       $y = -3x + 4$

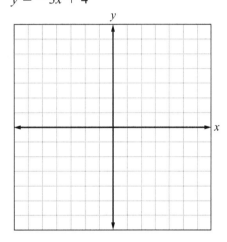

9. $y \leq 3x - 6$
   $2x + y > 3$

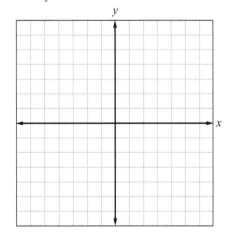

Solve.

_____ 10. Solve by substitution.

$$3x + 2y = -1$$
$$2x - y = 4$$

_____ 11. Solve by elimination.

$$x + y = 24$$
$$x - y = 48$$

Solve each system using the method of your choice.

_____ 12. $2x + 3y = 9$
$x - y = 2$

_____ 13. $4x - 5y = 4$
$-6x + 15y = -9$

14. Solve the system. Then classify it as inconsistent, consistent independent, or consistent dependent.

$y = 2x - 6$
$4x - 2y = 12$

_____ a. Solution

_____ b. Type

_____ 15. The difference of 3 times a first number and 4 times a second number is 34, while the difference of 4 times the first number and 3 times the second number is 43. Write and solve a system of equations to find the two numbers.

Joe flew 300 mi with the wind in 2 hr. After flying against the wind for 2 hr, however, he had made only 270 mi of the return trip.

16. Complete the table describing the problem. Let x represent the plane's speed with no wind and w represent the wind's speed.

	r	*t*	*d*
Returning with the Wind			
Going Against the Wind			

17. Write and solve a system of equations to find the speed of the plane with no wind and the wind's speed.

A grocery store has 12 lb of a trail mix that is 10% banana chips. The store's manager would like to add banana chips to bring the new mix up to 25% banana chips.

18. Complete the table below describing the mixtures. Let c represent pounds of banana chips and n represent pounds of new mix.

	Quantity	% Banana Chips	Amount of Banana Chips
Old Mix			
Banana Chips			
New Mix			

_____ 19. Write and solve a system of equations to find how many pounds of banana chips the manager needs to add.

_____ 20. Write the system of inequalities represented by the graph.

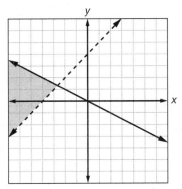

Name _____

Chapters 4-6

Second Quarter Exam

Multiple Choice. List all correct answers.

_____ 1. Which points are in quadrant IV?

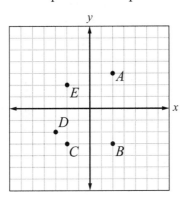

_____ 2. Which of the phrases can be interpreted as $\leq$?
 a. does not exceed
 b. at least
 c. is not more than
 d. is not greater than or equal to
 e. is at most

_____ 3. Which of the following lists contain(s) equivalent expressions?
 a. conjunction, and, $\vee$
 b. disjunction, and, $\vee$
 c. conjunction, or, $\wedge$
 d. disjunction, or, $\vee$
 e. conjunction, and, $\wedge$

_____ 4. Let $S = \{(2, 1), (3, 2), (-1, 4), (1, 2)\}$. Which of the following statements is true?
 a. S is neither a relation nor a function.
 b. S is both a relation and a function.
 c. S is a relation but not a function.
 d. S is a function but not a relation.
 e. None of the above

5. Which of the following relations is a function?

a.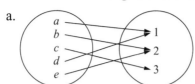

b.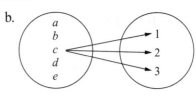

c.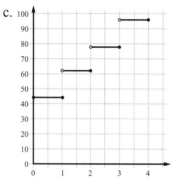

d.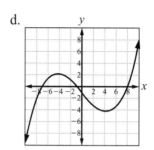

e. $\{(1, 2), (-1, 2), (3, 4), (-3, 4)\}$

6. Use the scatterplots to determine which statistic is the least predictive of success in college.

   a. ACT score
   b. the number of upper-level math and science courses
   c. high school GPA

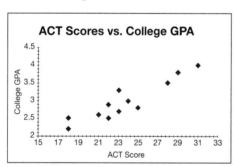

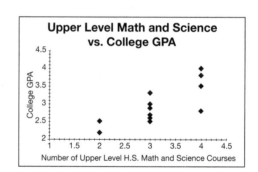

_____ 7. State the slope and *y*-intercept of $4x + 8y = 16$.

      a. $m = 2$; $(4, 0)$

      b. $m = \frac{1}{2}$; $(4, 0)$

      c. $m = -2$; $(0, 2)$

      d. $m = -\frac{1}{2}$; $(0, 2)$

      e. none of the above

8. Find the *x*- and *y*-intercepts of $3x - 2y = 6$ and use them to graph the equation.

_____ a. *x*-intercept

_____ b. *y*-intercept

c.

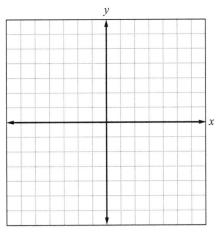

9. Sketch a graph of your city's average daily high temperature throughout the year.

Jan Feb Mar Apr May Jun Jul Aug Sep Oct Nov Dec

Solve and graph the following inequalities.

10. $3(3x - 4) \geq 7(2x + 3) + 2$

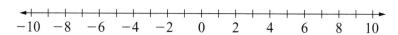

11. $3x + 2 \geq 8$ or $6x < x - 5$

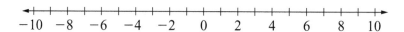

12. $2x + 7 < x + 11$ and
    $3x - 7 < 5x - 1$

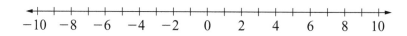

13. $|x + 5| < 3$

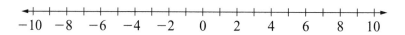

_____ 14. Write an absolute value equation representing all the numbers that are 7 units from -2. Then solve the equation.

_____ 15. Tornados have occurred on every continent except Antarctica. They occur most often between latitudes of 30° and 50°. Write a compound inequality describing the latitudes in which tornados are not likely to occur.

Write the function rule.

_____ 16. y varies directly with x and $y = 12$ when $x = 8$

_____ 17. y varies inversely with x and $y = 18$ when $x = 6$

_____ 18. Use the following table to find the function rule.

x	-3	-2	-1	0	1
y	-1	0	1	2	3

_____ 19. Write a function rule for the value of a new car, $V(t)$, if it costs \$31,500 when purchased and depreciates 10% of its original cost each year.

_____ 20. Write a function rule for an absolute value function that translates the vertex of $f(x) = |x|$ to $(4, -2)$.

Write the slope-intercept form of the equation of each line described below.

_____ 21. The line has a slope of -3 and passes through the point $(4, 5)$.

_____ 22. The line passes through the points $(4, 8)$ and $(-2, 6)$.

Write the slope–intercept form of the equation of each line described below.

_____ 23. The line passes through the point $(-2, 5)$ and is parallel to the line with the equation $y = -2x + 7$.

_____ 24. The line passes through the point $(1, 7)$ and is perpendicular to the line with the equation $3x + 21y = -2$.

25. Graph $12x + 3y < 6$.

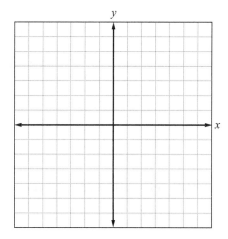

_____ 26. If a system of linear equations has at least two solutions, then which of the following statements is true? List all correct answers.

    a. The system is consistent.

    b. The system is inconsistent.

    c. The system is dependent.

    d. The system is independent.

    e. The system has more than two solutions.

_____ 27. Solve the system.

$$3x + 2y = 4$$
$$2x - y = 5$$

28. Graph the system of inequalities.

$$3x + 3y > 12$$
$$x - 2y < 6$$

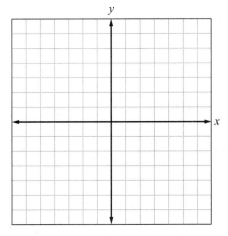

Write and solve a system of equations to answer the following questions.

29. Mendoza's Panadería makes two party platters. The $23 platter includes 2 dozen brownies and 3 dozen pastries, and the $56 platter includes 4 dozen brownies and 8 dozen pastries. What are the prices for each dozen brownies and each dozen pastries?

_____ a. price for a dozen brownies

_____ b. price for a dozen pastries

30. Pure oxygen is not safe to breathe for an extended period of time. Patients on a respirator will typically not receive a mixture of more than 40% oxygen. If regular air is 21% oxygen, how much pure oxygen and regular air (to the nearest tenth of a liter) should be combined to make 10 L of a 40% oxygen mixture?

_____ a. pure oxygen

_____ b. regular air

Chapter 8

Sections 1 & 2

True or false.

_____ 1. $(-m)^2 = -m^2$

_____ 2. $3x^{-3} = \dfrac{1}{3x^3}$

Simplify, leaving each answer in positive exponential form.

_____ 3. $(-3x^2y)(2xy^3)$

_____ 4. $\dfrac{(3xy^{-2})^2}{2x^{-3}y^3}$

_____ 5. $[(r^2)^3 r]^2$

_____ 6. Write a simplified algebraic expression for the height of the box.

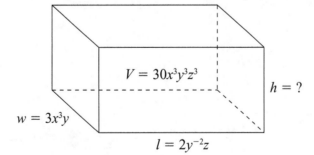

$V = 30x^3y^3z^3$

$h = ?$

$w = 3x^3y$

$l = 2y^{-2}z$

Chapter 8

Sections 3 & 4

_____ 1. Express 0.0021×10^{12} in scientific notation.

_____ 2. Simplify $(1.5 \times 10^{12})(8 \times 10^{-3})$, expressing the answer in scientific notation.

_____ 3. Simplify $(2.3 \times 10^{-7}) + (7.9 \times 10^{-8})$, expressing the answer in scientific notation.

_____ 4. On July 27, 2018, Mars will be about 57.6 million km from the earth. It will not be that close again until 2035. If a manned spacecraft could travel approximately 40,000 km/hr, how many days would it take the spacecraft to reach Mars from Earth?

5. Describe the translation of the graph of $y = x^2$ that produces the graph of $y = (x + 5)^2 + 3$.

6. Graph $y = (x + 3)^3 - 4$, clearly labeling the point of inflection.

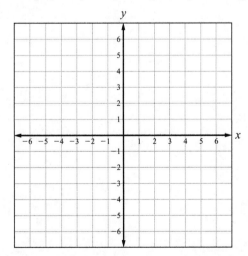

Chapter 8

Sections 5 & 6

_____ 1. Evaluate $y = \left(\frac{2}{3}\right)^x$ when $x = -2$.

_____ 2. Which of the following functions is increasing? List all correct answers.
  a. $y = 3(2)x$
  b. $y = -2x$
  c. $y = 2(0.5)^x$
  d. $y = 0.5(1.05)^x$

_____ 3. A town currently has a school-age population of 100,000 and expects that population to grow 8% annually. Write an exponential function modeling the town's school-age population.

_____ 4. If $6000 is invested in a certificate of deposit (CD) earning 6% APR compounded semiannually, determine the account balance after 20 yr.

_____ 5. Computers depreciate rapidly. If a new computer that costs $1200 loses 40% of its value every year, write a function to represent its value after t years. Then determine its worth 5 yr from now.

6. Which of the following tables represent(s) an exponential function? List all correct answers.

a.

x	0	1	2	3
y	0	0	0	0

b.

x	0	1	2	3
y	1	1	1	1

c.

x	0	1	2	3
y	1	2	4	8

d.

x	0	1	2	3
y	1	−1	1	−1

e.

x	0	1	2	3
y	1	2	3	4

Chapter 8

Test

True or false.

_____ 1. In a power function, the variable is in the exponent.

_____ 2. $x^a x^b = x^{ab}$

Simplify, leaving each answer in positive exponential form.

_____ 3. $5a^3(-2ab^2)^2$

_____ 4. $\dfrac{24x^2y^{-3}}{(2x^{-1}y^2)^3}$

_____ 5. $3m^3n^3 - 4m^{-2}n^5m^3n + 4mn^2m^2n + 6(mn^3)^2m^{-1}$

_____ 6. $xy^2(3x^{-1}y + 2xy^{-2}) - x^2y^{-2}(2y^2 + x^{-2}y^5)$

Simplify, expressing each answer in scientific notation.

_____ 7. $(3.2 \times 10^{12}) \div (1.6 \times 10^{-4})$

_____ 8. $(1.8 \times 10^{11}) - (9.2 \times 10^{10})$

_____ 9. If there are about 5×10^9 galaxies and every galaxy has about 1.5×10^9 stars, then about how many stars are in the universe?

_____ 10. What is the vertex of $f(x) = (x + 3)^2 + 4$?

_____ 11. Write a function rule for the graph of $y = x^3$ that is translated down 4 units and right 5 units.

12. Given $y = 5(3)^x$, state the following.

_____   a. the growth rate

_____   b. the growth factor

13. A bacterial culture, which initially contains 500 bacteria, doubles in size every day.

_____   a. Write an exponential function, $f(d)$, modeling the size of the culture after d days.

_____   b. How many bacteria are present after 10 days?

_____ 14. Write the equation of the graphed function.

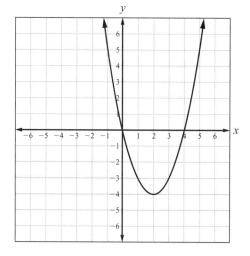

Use the following information to answer questions 15 and 16. The graph of $y = ab^x$ is decreasing and passes through the point (0, 4).

_____ 15. What is the value of a?

_____ 16. What values are possible for b?

_____ 17. The volume of a regular pyramid is one-third the area of the base times the height. If the base is a square with width $5xy^2$, what will the height have to be for the volume to be $125x^3y^3$?

_____ 18. How much money is in an account that earns 6% compounded quarterly if $10,000 is initially deposited and there are no withdrawals or additional deposits for 10 yr?

_____ 19. If Medicare cost the federal government about $430 billion in 2010 and Medicare costs grow at an annual rate of 13% over the next 50 yr, what will the cost of Medicare be in 2060 if no reforms are made?

_____ 20. The amount of a medication decreases in a patient's body by 8% each hour. If a patient took a 500 mg tablet of the medication and then took a 500 mg tablet again in 4 hr, how much of the medication (to the nearest milligram) would be in the patient's bloodstream 5 hr after he took the first tablet?

Chapter 9

Sections 1 & 2

For questions 1 and 2, classify each expression as a monomial, binomial, trinomial, other polynomial, or not a polynomial. Then state the degree of each polynomial.

_____ 1. $7x^3 + 4x$

_____ 2. $3x^2y^2 + 2x^2 + 3y^2 + 4$

_____ 3. Evaluate $p^5 - 3y^2 + 4m$ when $y = 3$, $m = -4$, and $p = 2$.

Simplify.

_____ 4. $(3x - 7y) + (7x + 4y)$

_____ 5. $(5x^2 + 3x - 6) - (2x^2 - 5x + 1)$

_____ 6. Write an expression for the perimeter of the polygon.

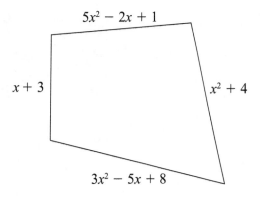

$5x^2 - 2x + 1$

$x + 3$

$x^2 + 4$

$3x^2 - 5x + 8$

Name _____

Multiply.

_____ 1. $4x^2(2x^2 - 3x + 5)$

_____ 2. $(3x - 2)(x - 5)$

_____ 3. $\begin{array}{r} 2x^2 + 4x - 1 \\ \times \qquad x + 3 \\ \hline \end{array}$

4. The figure models a multiplication of polynomials.

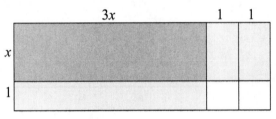

_____ a. Write the polynomial multiplication modeled by the diagram.

_____ b. Write the product.

_____ 5. When using the FOIL method to multiply $(2x + 3)(5x - 1)$, the product represented by the "I" is _____.
a. $(2x)(5x)$
b. $(2x)(-1)$
c. $(3)(5x)$
d. $(3)(-1)$
e. none of the above

_____ 6. Find the binomial that must be multiplied by $5x^3yz^2$ to obtain $15x^3y^2z^5 + 5x^3yz^2$.

Chapter 9

Sections 5 & 6

Simplify.

_____ 1. $(2x - 9)(2x + 9)$

_____ 2. $(4x + 1)^2$

_____ 3. $(12x^3 + 8x^2 + 24x) \div 4x$

_____ 4. $(x^3 + 3x - 5) \div (x - 3)$

_____ 5. What is the width of a rectangle if the area is $2x^2 - x - 6$ and the length is $2x + 3$?

_____ 6. Simplify $(x + 1)^2(x - 1)^2$.

Chapter 9

Test

Classify each expression as a monomial, binomial, trinomial, other polynomial, or not a polynomial. Then state the degree of each polynomial.

_____ 1. $-3x^4 + 9x^2 + 6$

_____ 2. $7x^3yz$

Evaluate each polynomial when $x = -3$, $y = 2$, and $z = 5$.

_____ 3. $x^2 - 5x + 3$

_____ 4. $4xy - 2yz$

Simplify.

_____ 5. $5x^2 + 3x^2$

_____ 6. $(7y^3 - 5) + (8 - 3y + 2y^3)$

_____ 7. $3x - (2x - 7)$

_____ 8. $(3a^2b - 4ab^2 + a^2b^2) - (2ab^2 + a^2b^2 + 5a^2b)$

_____ 9. $(13m^3n)(5m^2n^2)$

_____ 10. $-3x(2x^2 - xy + 4y^2)$

_____ 11. $(x - 5)(2x^2 + 7x - 3)$

_____ 12. $(z + 12)(z - 12)$

_____ 13. $(2x + 3y)(4x - 5y)$

_____ 14. $(3x + 4)^2$

_____ 15. $\dfrac{4r^5s^2 - 6r^2s^3}{2r^2s^2}$

_____ 16. $\dfrac{y^2 - 6y + 11}{y - 2}$

17. Use FOIL to fill in the blanks when multiplying $(3x + 5)(2x - 1)$.

$(3x + 5)(2x - 1) = $ ___ $+$ ___ $+$ ___ $+$ ___
$\quad\quad\quad\quad\quad\quad\quad\quad$ F $\quad$ O $\quad$ I $\quad$ L

_____ 18. Which of the following terms could be combined with $2x^2y$? List all correct answers.

a. $2xy$
b. $-2x(xy)$
c. $2yx^2$
d. $2xy^2$
e. $5x^2y$

_____ 19. What is the highest possible degree of the remainder when a polynomial with a degree of nine is divided by a polynomial with a degree of four?

a. 5
b. 4
c. 3
d. 1
e. 0

_____ 20. What is the height of a box if the width is $x + 1$, the length is $x + 3$, and the volume is $x^3 + 6x^2 + 11x + 6$?

Chapter 10

Sections 1 & 2

_____ 1. Find the GCF of $75x^2y$ and $45xy^2$.

For questions 2–5, factor each polynomial. If the polynomial will not factor, write "prime."

_____ 2. $a^3b + a^2b^2 + ab^3$

_____ 3. $x^2 - 11x + 24$

_____ 4. $y^2 + 18y + 72$

_____ 5. $2z^2 - 16z - 40$

_____ 6. If $x^2 - ax - b$ factors as $(x - c)(x + d)$, how does $x^2 + ax - b$ factor?

Algebra 1

Chapter 10

Sections 3 & 4

Factor.

_____ 1. $6a^2 - ab - b^2$

_____ 2. $6r^2 - 26r - 20$

_____ 3. $16x^2 - 24x + 9$

_____ 4. $4y^2 - 9$

5. What is the first step in factoring any polynomial?

_____ 6. Fill in the blank to make $z^8 +$ _____ $+ 144$ a perfect square trinomial.

Chapter 10

Section 5

Factor completely.

_____ 1. $a^3b - 4a^2b^2 - 5ab^3$

_____ 2. $x^4 - y^4$

_____ 3. $a(b + c) + d(b + c)$

_____ 4. $y^3 - y^2 - 4y + 4$

_____ 5. $ab + 2b - 12a - 24$

_____ 6. $(x^2 + 2x + 1) - (y^2 - 4y + 4)$

Chapter 10

Test

Multiple Choice. List all correct answers.

_____ 1. Which of the following is a perfect square?
   a. $x^2 + 6x + 9$
   b. $w^4 - 4w + 4$
   c. $x^2y^2 - 2xy + 1$
   d. $z^6 + 25z^3 + 25$

_____ 2. Which of the following is a difference of squares?
   a. $s^6 - s^4$
   b. $9t^2 - 4r^2$
   c. $16w^3 - 9s^4$
   d. $25x^{12}y^6 - 9w^{10}z^4$

_____ 3. Find the GCF of $12x^3y$ and $21x^2y^2$.
   a. $84x^3y^2$
   b. $84x^2y$
   c. $3x^3y^2$
   d. $3x^2y$

Factor the common monomial.

_____ 4. $96z^5 + 72z^3 - 48z^2$

_____ 5. $a^5b^3 - a^4b^4 - 2a^2b^6$

Factor the difference of squares.

_____ 6. $36y^2 - 1$

_____ 7. $25v^6 - 9w^2$

Factor the perfect square trinomials.

_____ 8. $c^2 - 6c + 9$

_____ 9. $4y^2 + 4yz + z^2$

Factor the following trinomials.

_____ 10. $x^2 + 14x + 33$

_____ 11. $w^2 - 7w - 18$

_____ 12. $2a^2 - a + 3$

_____ 13. $6n^2 + 13n - 28$

Factor by grouping.

_____ 14. $x(3y + 1) - 2(3y + 1)$

_____ 15. $8x^3 - 6x^2 + 4x - 3$

For questions 16–22, factor completely. If the polynomial will not factor over the set of integers, write "prime."

_____ 16. $y^2 + 1$

_____ 17. $a^3 - 4a^2 + 4a$

_____ 18. $6r^2 + 11r - 10$

_____ 19. $4x^5 + 8x^4 + 8x^3$

_____ 20. $2c^4 + 12c^2 + 18$

_____ 21. $5x^2 - 5xy - 10y^2$

_____ 22. $a^3 + 4a^2 - 9a - 36$

_____ 23. The formula for the surface area of a cone can be stated $S = \frac{1}{2}cr + \frac{1}{2}cl$. Rewrite this formula by factoring the right side of the equation.

24. Express the area of the entire rectangle as a product of binomials.

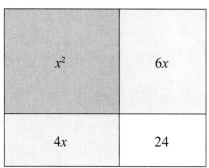

25. Given $(x + y)$ is a factor, factor $x^3 + y^3$.

Chapters 8-10

Third Quarter Exam

_____ 1. True or false. $-x^4 = (-x)^4$

_____ 2. Classify the expression $2x^2y + 3xy - 7$ as monomial, binomial, trinomial, other polynomial, or not a polynomial. Then state its degree.

_____ 3. Simplify $\dfrac{3x^{-2}(yz)^2}{-3^2(xyz)^{-1}}$, leaving the answer in positive exponential form.

_____ 4. Simplify $\left(\dfrac{3xz^{-1}}{y}\right)^2\left(\dfrac{4xy}{z^2}\right)$, leaving all variables in the numerator.

_____ 5. Convert 3421.56×10^{-5} to scientific notation.

_____ 6. Write a function rule for the graph of $y = x^2$ that is translated right 3 units and down 4 units.

_____ 7. What is the value of $10,000 invested at 8% compounded quarterly for 10 yr?

_____ 8. If a 4 oz colony of mold could grow to 5 oz in one day, how large would the colony become in one week?

Simplify.

_____ 9. $(3x^2 - 5x + 7) - (x^2 - 9x - 6)$

_____ 10. $4a^2b(3ab^4 + 2a^2b^2)$

_____ 11. $(2x + 3)(4x - 7)$

_____ 12. $(3x + 5z)^2$

_____ 13. $(x + 5)(2x^2 - 3x + 4)$

_____ 14. $(6x^3 - 5x^2 + 8x - 12) \div (x - 3)$

Multiple Choice.

_____ 15. When using the FOIL method to multiply $(ax + b)(cx + d)$, the product represented by "O" is _____.
   a. acx^2
   b. adx
   c. bcx
   d. bd
   e. none of the above

_____ 16. What value of k makes $4x^2 + 12x + k$ a perfect square trinomial?
   a. 3
   b. 6
   c. 9
   d. 12
   e. 36

Factor. If the polynomial will not factor over the integers, write "prime."

_____ 17. $16x^2 - 25$

_____ 18. $4a^5b^3 + 24a^3b^5 - 16a^2b$

_____ 19. $x^2 - 12x + 36$

_____ 20. $x^2 - 12x + 1$

_____ 21. $2x^2 - x - 15$

Factor. If the polynomial will not factor over the integers, write "prime."

_____ 22. $6x^2 - 19xy + 10y^2$

_____ 23. $am + bm - an - bn$

_____ 24. $3x^3 - 15x^2 + 18x$

25. A millionaire is going golfing and asks you to caddy (carry his clubs) for him. He will pay you either $100 per hole or 2¢ for the first hole, 4¢ for the second hole, 8¢ for the third hole, etc. Assuming there are 18 holes to be played, calculate how much you would be paid on the 18th hole if you chose the second method. Which method of payment would you choose? Explain why.

Chapter 11

Sections 1 & 2

Simplify.

_____ 1. $\sqrt[3]{-64}$

_____ 2. $\sqrt{180}$

_____ 3. $\sqrt{18y^5}$

_____ 4. Convert $\sqrt[3]{3x^2y}$ to exponential form.

_____ 5. Mentally estimate $\sqrt{40}$ to the nearest integer.

_____ 6. Convert $4^{\frac{1}{3}}x^{\frac{1}{6}}y^{\frac{1}{2}}$ to radical form.

Chapter 11

Sections 3 & 4

Simplify. Assume that all variables in the radicand represent nonnegative values.

_____ 1. $\sqrt{75}\sqrt{6}$

_____ 2. $\sqrt[3]{18x^2y}\sqrt[3]{24x^4y^4}$

_____ 3. $\dfrac{3\sqrt{8}}{\sqrt{12}}$

_____ 4. $\sqrt{3x^3y} \div \sqrt{12xy^3}$

_____ 5. The width of a rectangle is $4\sqrt{6}$, and its length is $2\sqrt{15}$. Express its area as a simplified radical.

_____ 6. A water tower is made in the shape of a sphere. Use the formula $r = \sqrt[3]{\dfrac{3V}{4\pi}}$ to determine its radius if the volume needs to be $36{,}000\pi$ ft^3.

Chapter 11

Sections 5 & 6

Simplify. Assume that all variables in the radicand represent nonnegative values.

_____   1. $2\sqrt{3} - 5\sqrt{12} + 8\sqrt{75}$

_____   2. $12a\sqrt{3a^3} + 4\sqrt{32a^7} - 8a^2\sqrt{27a} - 7a^2\sqrt{18a^3}$

_____   3. Find the midpoint of a segment with the endpoints $(3, 8)$ and $(-7, 2)$.

_____   4. Find the distance between $(4, 9)$ and $(9, -3)$.

_____   5. Find the length of the unknown side of a right triangle in which the hypotenuse $c = 11$ cm and side $a = 2\sqrt{10}$ cm.

6. Are $(7, 11)$, $(9, 15)$, and $(11, 14)$ the vertices of a right triangle? Show all work.

Sections 7 & 8

Simplify.

_____   1. $(\sqrt{3} - \sqrt{5})(\sqrt{6} + \sqrt{10})$

_____   2. $\dfrac{6}{3 - \sqrt{5}}$

_____   3. $(\sqrt{2xz} - 2\sqrt{z})(\sqrt{2z} + \sqrt{xz})$

Solve.

_____   4. $\sqrt{x - 3} = 8$

_____   5. $2\sqrt{x + 1} + 3 = 7$

_____   6. The amount of production at a meat processing plant is modeled by $P = 300 + 50\sqrt{t - 40}$, where P represents production and t represents the number of hours worked by each employee. If the company needs to set the production level to 400, how many hours should be scheduled for each employee?

Section 9

Chapter 11

Determine the domain of each radical function.

_____ 1. $f(x) = \sqrt{x + 8} - 5$ _____ 2. $f(x) = \sqrt{-2x + 8} - 5$

Write a function rule for the translation or reflection of $f(x) = \sqrt{x}$.

_____ 3. translated 3 units right and 5 units down

_____ 4. reflected across the y-axis

Graph.

5. $f(x) = \sqrt{x + 2} - 2$

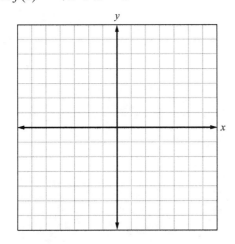

6. $f(x) = -\sqrt{x} + 2$

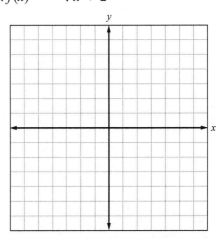

Chapter 11

Test

Simplify. If the expression is not a real number, state "not real." Assume that variables in the radicand are nonnegative.

_____ 1. $\sqrt{25}$ _____ 2. $\sqrt[3]{-108}$

_____ 3. $\sqrt{-49}$ _____ 4. $\sqrt{24x^3y}$

_____ 5. $\sqrt{12x^3y}\sqrt{75xy^3}$ _____ 6. $\sqrt{3xy^2} \div \sqrt{12x^2y}$

_____ 7. $\dfrac{5}{3 + \sqrt{2}}$ _____ 8. $(\sqrt{2x} + \sqrt{4y})(\sqrt{5x} - \sqrt{10y})$

_____ 9. $\sqrt{3a^2b^3} - ab\sqrt{27b} + 4\sqrt{9a^4b^2} + a\sqrt{12b^3}$

Solve. If there is no solution, state "no solution."

_____ 10. $\sqrt{2x + 1} = 3$ _____ 11. $\sqrt{x + 3} + 7 = 3$

_____ 12. $3\sqrt{2x - 2} + 7 = 13$

Find the length of the unknown side of each right triangle if *c* is the hypotenuse.

_____ 13. $a = \sqrt{28}, b = 6, c = ?$ _____ 14. $a = 3\sqrt{7}, c = 12, b = ?$

_____ 15. Find the distance between $(5, 2)$ and $(-3, 4)$.

_____ 16. Mentally estimate $\sqrt{150}$ to the nearest integer.

_____ 17. Find the midpoint of $(8, -3)$ and $(2, 9)$.

_____ 18. What is the domain of $f(x) = \sqrt{x + 3} + 4$?

_____ 19. Write a function rule that reflects the graph of $f(x) = \sqrt{x}$ across the y-axis and then translates the graph 5 units up.

_____ 20. Convert $\sqrt[3]{27x^2y}$ to exponential form.

_____ 21. Convert $5^{\frac{1}{4}}x^{\frac{1}{2}}$ to radical form.

_____ 22. The instantaneous velocity of a free-falling object can be calculated using the formula $v = \sqrt{2gd}$, where g is the gravitational acceleration of 32 ft/sec² and d is the distance the object has traveled in feet. Find the velocity of a boy who hits the ground after he jumps from a 16 ft roof.

_____ 23. A 50 ft ladder needs to reach a building 20 ft away. How high up the building (to the nearest tenth of a foot) will it reach?

24. Graph $f(x) = \sqrt{x + 4} - 3$.

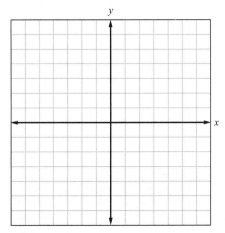

25. Are (2, 5), (5, 9), and (9, 6) the vertices of a right triangle? Show all work.

Chapter 12

Sections 1 & 2

Solve.

_____ 1. $x(x - 1)(x + 2) = 0$ _____ 2. $z^2 + 9z = 10$

_____ 3. $6x^2 + 5x - 6 = 0$

Solve by taking roots.

_____ 4. $8y^2 = 32$ _____ 5. $(x + 5)^2 = 15$

_____ 6. The length of a rectangle is 4 in. more than twice the width. If the total area is 30 in.^{2}, what is the width of the rectangle?

Chapter 12

Sections 3 & 4

What number must be added to complete the square?

_____ 1. $x^2 - 12x$

_____ 2. $x^2 + 3x$

Solve by completing the square.

_____ 3. $a^2 + 6a = 27$

_____ 4. $2m^2 + 14m = 16$

_____ 5. $3x^2 + 6x + 303 = 0$

_____ 6. The height of a projectile (in feet) is modeled by $h(t) = -16t^2 + v_i t + h_i$, where v_i is the initial vertical velocity (in feet per second) and h_i is the initial height (in feet). If a shell leaves a cannon at ground level going straight up at 800 ft/sec, when is the shell at a height of 3600 ft?

Sections 5 & 6

Chapter 12

_____ 1. Which choice best describes the solutions to $3x^2 + 5x + 2 = 0$?
a. two rational
b. two irrational
c. one rational
d. no real

Use the quadratic formula to solve.

_____ 2. $x^2 + 3x - 10 = 0$

_____ 3. $2x^2 + 9x = 4$

_____ 4. Solve $8y^2 + 20y - 12 = 0$ by using the method of your choice.

_____ 5. What are the dimensions of a rectangle whose perimeter is 70 in. and whose area is 300 in.²?

Write a quadratic equation in standard form with the given solutions.

_____   6. $x = 3, \frac{1}{2}$

Chapter 12

Sections 7 & 8

Fill in the blank.

_____   1. The graph of $f(x) = -3x^2 - 7$ opens _____.

_____   2. The vertex of $f(x) = 2(x + 5)^2 + 2$ is _____.

3. Let $g(x) = x^2 + 4x - 7$.

_____   Write $g(x)$ in graphing form.

_____   The graph of $g(x)$ _____ the graph of $f(x) = x^2$.
   a. is steeper than
   b. is flatter than
   c. has the same shape as

The profit resulting from manufacturing and selling a product is represented by the function $P(x) = -30(x - 500)^2 + 1000$, where x is the number of products manufactured and $P(x)$ is the profit generated.

_____   4. How much profit is gained (or lost) by manufacturing 450 items?

_____   5. How many items should be produced for maximum profit, and what is the maximum profit?

6. Graph $f(x) = -2x^2 - 8x - 6$.

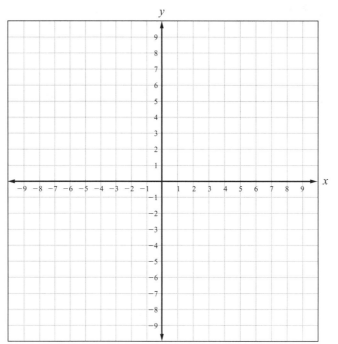

Section 9

Chapter 12

Find the *y*-intercept and zeros of the following functions.

_____ 1. $f(x) = 6x^2 - 5x - 6$

_____ 2. $f(x) = -3(x + 2)^2 + 2$

Let $f(x) = ax^2 + bx + c = a(x - h)^2 + k$ for questions 3 and 4.

_____ 3. If $a > 0$ and $c < 0$, how many real zeros will $f(x)$ have?

_____ 4. If $k < 0$, for what values of a will $f(x)$ have no real zeros?

Let $P(x) = -50x^2 + 20{,}000x - 1{,}500{,}000$ represent the profit function for manufacturing a particular model of recreational vehicle (RV) and x represent the number of RVs produced monthly.

_____ 5. How many RVs should be produced to maximize profit? What is that profit?

_____ 6. Use a compound inequality to state the range of the number of RVs that need to be sold each month for the company to make a profit.

Chapter 12

_____ 1. Solve $(x - 3)(x - 6) = 0$.

_____ 2. Solve $2x^2 + 9x = 18$ by factoring.

_____ 3. Solve $5(x - 10)^2 = 100$ by taking roots.

_____ 4. Solve $x^2 - 10x = 39$ by completing the square.

_____ 5. Solve $2x^2 + 8x = -3$ by using the quadratic formula.

Solve the following equations using the method of your choice.

_____ 6. $(2x + 5)(3x - 7) = 0$ _____ 7. $x^2 = 49$

_____ 8. $x^2 - 3x - 28 = 0$ _____ 9. $x^2 + 7x - 3 = 0$

_____ 10. $4x^2 - 8x = 5$

Use $f(x) = a(x - h)^2 + k = ax^2 + bx + c$ for questions 11–13.

_____ 11. If $a < 0$, the graph of $f(x)$ opens _____.

_____ 12. The vertex of $f(x)$ is _____.

_____ 13. The y-intercept of the graph of $f(x)$ is _____.

_____ 14. What number must be added to $x^2 + 28x$ to complete the square?

_____ 15. Write a quadratic equation that has roots of 3 and -1.

_____ 16. What are the dimensions of a rectangle if its perimeter is 48 ft and its
                            area is 80 ft^2?

The height of a projectile (in feet) is modeled by $h(t) = -16t^2 + v_i t + h_i$, where v_i is the initial vertical velocity (in feet per second) and h_i is the initial height (in feet). A baseball is shot upward from the ground at an initial velocity of 100 ft/sec.

_____ 17. Write the function that models the height of the baseball at time t.

_____ 18. When will the baseball hit the ground?

_____ 19. What will be the maximum height of the ball?

Use $f(x) = x^2 + 2x - 3$ for questions 20–25.

20. Calculate the discriminant of $f(x)$ and describe its roots.

_____ $D = ?$

_____   The function has _____ root(s).
a. two rational   b. two irrational
c. one rational   d. one irrational
e. no real

_____   21. Find the zeros of the function.

_____   22. Complete the square to write $f(x)$ in graphing form.

_____   23. State the coordinates of the graph's vertex.

_____   24. Is the vertex a maximum or a minimum?

25. Graph $f(x)$.

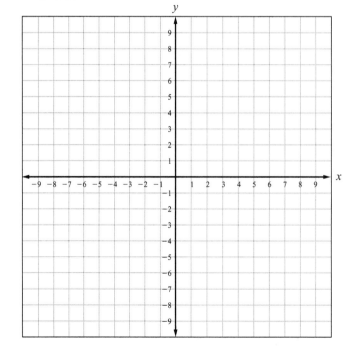

Chapter 13

Sections 1 & 2

True or false.

_____ 1. $\dfrac{w + 1}{w} = \dfrac{\cancel{w} + 1}{\cancel{w}} = 1$

State any excluded values.

_____ 2. $\dfrac{3x^3 + 5x + 1}{x^2 - 5x + 6}$

Simplify, leaving each answer in factored form.

_____ 3. $\dfrac{x^2 - 4x + 4}{x^2 - 4}$

_____ 4. $\dfrac{2x^2 - x - 3}{x^2 + x - 2} \cdot \dfrac{x^2 + 2x - 3}{x^2 - x - 2}$

_____ 5. $\dfrac{3x^2 - 3}{2x^2 + 6x + 4} \div \dfrac{3x^2 - 9x + 6}{4x^2 - 16}$

_____ 6. Write a rational expression representing the portion of the figure that is shaded. State the result as a simplified expression and as a percent (to the nearest tenth).

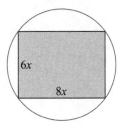

Sections 3 & 4

_____ 1. Find the LCM of $x^2 + 5x + 6$ and $2x^2 - 18$. Leave your answer in factored form.

_____ 2. Which of the following expressions is equivalent to $\dfrac{2 - x}{x - 3}$? List all correct answers.

    a. $\dfrac{2 - x}{3 - x}$

    b. $\dfrac{x - 2}{3 - x}$

    c. $\dfrac{x - 2}{x - 3}$

    d. $-\dfrac{x - 2}{x - 3}$

    e. $\dfrac{2 + x}{x + 3}$

Perform the indicated operations and simplify. Leave the answers in factored form.

_____ 3. $\dfrac{3x + 2}{x^2 - x} - \dfrac{x + 4}{x^2 - x}$

_____ 4. $\dfrac{3x + 5}{x^2 + 9x - 10} + \dfrac{x - 2}{2x^2 + x - 3}$

_____ 5. $\dfrac{-2x}{x^2 - 1} + \dfrac{3}{x + 1} - \dfrac{x - 1}{x^2 + 2x + 1}$

_____ 6. Find the difference in the heights of the two rectangles in the figure below.

h_1 | Area $= x + 2$
$w_1 = x^2 + 7x + 10$

Area $= x + 4$ h_2
$w_2 = x^2 + 3x - 4$

Chapter 13

Sections 5 & 6

Simplify.

_____ 1. $4 + \dfrac{x}{x + 2}$

_____ 2. $\dfrac{\dfrac{x^2 - r^2}{x - r}}{x + r}$

_____ 3. $\dfrac{1 - \dfrac{1}{x}}{1 + \dfrac{1}{x}}$

Solve.

_____ 4. $\dfrac{3x + 5}{x - 1} = 4$

_____ 5. $\dfrac{6}{2y + 3} = \dfrac{3}{y - 1}$

_____ 6. $\dfrac{x + 2}{x} - \dfrac{4}{x + 1} = \dfrac{x + 5}{x^2 + x}$

Chapter 13

Sections 7 & 8

Let $f(x) = \dfrac{3}{x-4} + 2$ for questions 1–4.

_____ 1. State the horizontal asymptote of $f(x)$.

_____ 2. State the vertical asymptote of $f(x)$.

_____ 3. State the center of $f(x)$.

4. Graph $f(x)$.

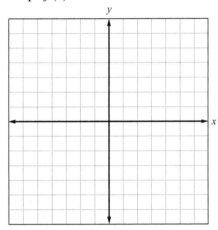

_____ 5. On the Olsen farm an old combine can harvest the wheat fields in 8 days. Recently the farm bought a new combine that can do the same job in 5 days. How many days will it take to harvest the fields using both combines?

_____ 6. Jack wants to measure the distance between his scout camp and another camp upstream. He can paddle his kayak at a rate of 5 mi/hr in still water, and the rate of the river is 3 mi/hr. If it takes Jack 10 hr to paddle to the camp and back, how far is the camp?

Chapter 13

Test

Multiple Choice.

_____ 1. For which of the following rational expression operations must you first find a common denominator? List all correct answers.

    a. addition
    b. division
    c. multiplication
    d. subtraction

_____ 2. Classify the function $f(x) = \frac{\sqrt{x}}{3} + 1$.

    a. absolute value
    b. exponential
    c. linear
    d. radical
    e. rational

_____ 3. State the excluded values for the expression $\dfrac{(x-5)^2}{2(x-5)(x+5)}$.

_____ 4. Given the individual rates of workers, to find the combined rate of all the individuals working together you must _____ the individual rates.

_____ 5. What is the LCM of $6x^3(x+1)$ and $15x^5(x-1)$?

_____ 6. When a rational equation simplifies to $8 = 7$, the equation has _____.

Let $f(x) = \frac{7}{x-1} - 5.$

7. State the horizontal and vertical asymptotes of $f(x)$.

_____   a. the horizontal asymptote

_____   b. the vertical asymptote

_____ 8. State the center of $f(x)$.

Simplify, leaving the answers in factored form.

_____ 9. $\dfrac{y^2z - yz^2}{y + z} \div \dfrac{y^2 - z^2}{y^2 + 2yz + z^2}$

_____ 10. $\dfrac{x^2 - 10x + 25}{2x^2 - 50}$

_____ 11. $\dfrac{4x^2}{x - y} - \dfrac{4y^2}{x - y}$

_____ 12. $3 + \dfrac{-xy + y^2}{x^2 - y^2}$

_____ 13. $\dfrac{2 + \frac{x}{2}}{\frac{x^2 - 16}{8}}$

_____ 14. $\dfrac{3x + 2}{x + 1} + \dfrac{7}{x - 4} - \dfrac{35}{x^2 - 3x - 4}$

_____ 15. Solve $\dfrac{9}{x + 1} - \dfrac{2}{x - 1} = 1$.

_____ 16. After completing several tests, quizzes, and homework assignments, Tami currently has a 78% out of 700 points in Algebra 1. If Tami can earn a 90% for the rest of the semester, how many more points need to be in the semester for Tami to raise her grade to an 80%?

_____ 17. In 1931 Frank Wykoff ran the 100 yd dash in 9.3 sec. Although this should have been a world record, his time was disqualified because officials believed that it was impossible for a human to run that fast. How fast (to the nearest mile per hour) did Frank Wykoff run?

_____ 18. Jay rode his motorcycle 100 mi into the mountains. On the return trip he was able to average 5 mi/hr faster. If the round trip took 5 hr, how fast (to the nearest mile per hour) did he travel going each way?

19. Stevens and Sons Painting won the bid to paint 4 identical houses. Mr. Stevens painted the first house in 5 days. Each of his two sons took 4.5 days to paint a house. Working together, how long will it take to paint the last house?

_____

20. Graph $f(x) = \dfrac{3}{x + 2} + 1$.

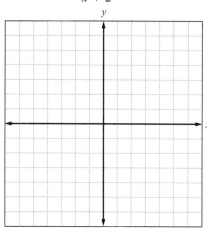

Fourth Quarter Exam

Simplify.

_____ 1. $\sqrt[3]{-\frac{8}{27}}$

_____ 2. $\sqrt{72x^8y^3}$

_____ 3. $4\sqrt{6}(2\sqrt{15}) - \sqrt{2}(3\sqrt{5} - \sqrt{2})$

_____ 4. $\frac{4 - \sqrt{2}}{4 + \sqrt{2}}$

_____ 5. $\frac{5a^2 - 25}{5}$

Simplify.

_____ 6. $\dfrac{x^2 - 1}{x^2 - 4x + 4} \div \dfrac{x^2 + 3x + 2}{x^2 - 4}$

_____ 7. $\dfrac{x + 1}{x - \dfrac{1}{x}}$

_____ 8. $\dfrac{x + 2}{x^2 - 1} + \dfrac{x}{x^2 - 2x - 3} + \dfrac{3}{x^2 - 4x + 3}$

Solve.

_____ 9. $(2x - 3)(x + 6) = 0$

_____ 10. $\sqrt{4x + 5} - 12 = -5$

_____ 11. $\dfrac{2x + 5}{x - 3} = 2$

_____ 12. $\dfrac{x}{x - 3} - \dfrac{18}{x^2 - 9} = \dfrac{2x}{x + 3}$

_____ 13. Solve $x^2 - 12x + 12 = 0$ by completing the square.

_____ 14. Solve $2x^2 = 7x - 3$ by using the quadratic formula.

_____ 15. Find a.

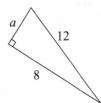

_____ 16. Find the distance between the points $(6, -9)$ and $(5, -3)$.

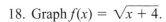 17. Find the midpoint of the line segment with the endpoints $(\sqrt{18}, 6)$ and $(-\sqrt{50}, 11)$.

18. Graph $f(x) = \sqrt{x + 4}$.

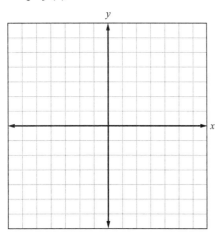

19. Graph $g(x) = (x - 3)^2 - 4$.

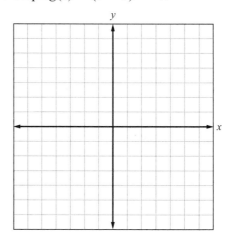

20. Graph $h(x) = \frac{6}{x} + 1$.

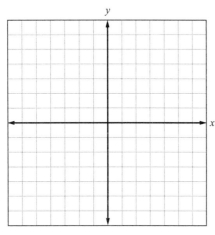

21. Below is the graph of $y = s(x)$. On the same coordinate axis, graph $y = -s(x)$.

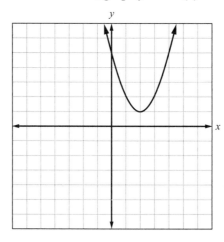

The profit resulting from the monthly manufacturing and selling of a furnace is represented by the function $P(x) = -2x^2 + 1000x - 45{,}000$, where x is the number of products manufactured and $P(x)$ is the profit generated. Use $P(x)$ for questions 22 and 23.

_____ 22. How many items should be produced for maximum profit, and what is the maximum profit?

_____ 23. The break-even point is the point where a company neither makes a profit nor loses money, i.e., where the profit is zero. What are the break-even points for the sale of this furnace?

_____ 24. Mr. Simmons figures he can paint his house in 5 days. If his son helps, together they can paint it in 2 days. How long will it take his son to paint the house if he works alone?

_____ 25. Damon and Peter, who paddle a canoe at 4 mi/hr in still water, took 8 hr to paddle 9 mi upstream and then return. Complete the table below, and then write and solve an equation to determine the speed of the river's current.

	r	t	d
Upstream			
Downstream			